Spe
The Good Witch
Of Pendle

Reliable Magic
for Success in
All Circumstances

Joyce Froome

First published in 2018
by Palatine Books,
Carnegie House,
Chatsworth Road
Lancaster LA1 4SL
www.palatinebooks.com

British Library Cataloguing-in-Publication data
A catalogue record for this book is available from the British Library

ISBN 13: 978-1-910837-18-4

Designed and typeset by Carnegie Book Production
www.carnegiepublishing.co.uk

Printed and bound by Jellyfish Solutions

Author's Note

Many people who practised magic compiled their own notebooks of spells and charms. Although no book of magic associated with the Pendle witches has survived, this is an imagining of what a book written by Jennet Device might have been like.

The spells are based on authentic records, but are of course for entertainment only, as a reflection of our ancestors' traditional beliefs. For more information about their sources and the history of folk magic, see my book *Wicked Enchantments: A History of the Pendle Witches and Their Magic* (Palatine Books, 2010).

Acknowledgments

Special thanks to all the Carnegie team,
in particular Anna Goddard for telling me
to make the book longer, and to Srishti
Kadu for her brilliant work on the layout;
also to my brother Peter for telling me
to add more pictures; to the fine cats,
dogs and other animals who inspired the
illustrations; to Jennet Device herself,
and all the cunning folk whose stories
feature here; and to the many other people
who have given me so much support,
encouragement and inspiration, enabling
this book to go beyond my original plan,
and become (I hope) an expression of
Jennet's magical world.

art of magic? When you were a child you would have bled to death if the wizard Edmund Hartlay had not stopped the bleeding by putting a bone from a dead man's hand in the wound.

That may be so (he replied), but the wizard also conjured up a devil from Hell ~ a thing like a Black Dog. And, as you well know, Jennet, your brother James inherited

this demon as his
familiar spirit, calling
it Daun Dhu ~ that is,
the Dark Lord.

Is this not proof, Jennet, that all your skills come from the Devil? Like Eve, you have been seduced by him to covet knowledge that is forbidden by God. And you are so blinded by pride that so long as your neighbours are in awe of you, the damnation of your soul is of no importance.

If you think my neighbours are in awe of me (I said) you know very little about the folk of Pendle, even though you are their magistrate.

When they come to me for healing they complain of their sores and fevers, their tooth-aches and bone-lameness, at such length that it would make you sick to listen to them.

But when I have cured them, it is: What, Jennet, you think I will give you a chicken? When all you did was say a charm, sprinkle salt and savory on my wrist, and give me a medicine made of rue? When next I do some baking maybe I will send you half a loaf.

If I was full of pride (I said) I would not cure such people ~ I would send them away owl-blasted.

So you admit (said he) that you can curse as well as cure?

I could if I wished (I replied). It would take more provocation than my neighbours are capable of ~ but no doubt someone of your importance could manage it.

I returned home seething with such anger that it all but choked me. As I opened my door Daun Dhu appeared, and (looking at me closely) he said: Ah, Jennet, I hoped you would act the diplomat with John Starkie, but I see you are full of thoughts of retaliation against him.

He lay down by the hearth and continued: When the Pope first declared that the art of magic was a crime punishable by death, the Angel Hocroel appeared to the magician Honorius and advised him to write a book of magic. What better revenge could there be, than to ensure that the art of magic would not only survive, but be spread by copies of this book all across the world?
.

Now, you have knowledge of a great many spells and charms, stones and herbs and so forth, that could be very profitable to your fellow cunning folk in Pendle Forest, and indeed across England. Would it not be a fine way to repay John Starkie for his persecution of you, to set down all that knowledge in a book? And I would be happy to assist

you, just as Hocroel
assisted Honorius, even
though I am not an
Angel from Heaven,
but only a Lord of
Elfland.

And so I have
resolved to do as
Daun Dhu suggested.

The Virtues of the Herb Vervain~

Daun Dhu has taught me much of what I know, in particular the virtues of the herb vervain, which is the most valuable of all the herbs. (And when it is dried, the leaf turns most strangely to a white colour, like sea-foam.)

It cleanses and heals any wound on or within the body.

It casts out worms and stones.

It eases fevers.

If you carry it with you, it will protect you from any evil spell directed against you.

Elf Darts and Other Stones~

Also, Daun Dhu gave me an elf dart, which they make in Elfland very skilfully out of a fine stone (for they never use iron~indeed, it dispels the power of their magic).

If you place an elf dart in a bowl, and pour water over it, you may give the water to any sick animal to drink, and it will cure him.

And there is another stone that has the same virtue, and it is shaped like a ram's horn.

The Thunderbolt ~

This is a stone about the size of a woman's hand, either black or yellowish, and some~ what glassy from the great heat it generates as it is hurled to earth.

If you pour water over it, anyone who drinks the water will be cured of pain and stiffness in the joints.

And as long as you have one of these thunderbolts in your house, no other thunderbolt will ever strike it.

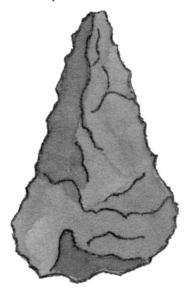

The Dragon Stone~

This is found in the head of a dragon. It is a grey colour, and has within it, white like fine salt, the symbol that is called the Seal of King Solomon, or the Pentacle.

Anyone who carries this stone will always have victory in battle or in a court of law.

Some people say that the dragon must be alive when the stone is taken. Indeed, whenever you take something from an animal for magic it is best if it is done so that he can be let go alive. But from what I have seen of those who sell Dragon Stones I doubt if they have the wit or courage to take a stone from the head of a living dragon.

Rather, I have heard that there are places where falls of rock reveal the bones of dragons long dead, and I think these stones are taken from such places.

The Toad Stone ~

If you place a toad on a red cloth he will vomit up a small grey stone.

Set this stone in a ring and it will have these virtues ~

It will protect whoever wears it from poison.

It will cure the bites and stings of venomous beasts.

Stones from within a Swallow~

Within the body of a young swallow taken from the nest there are three stones, one brown, one red and one white.

If you give the brown stone to a woman in childbirth, she will immediately be delivered.

If you would ask a favour of someone, hold the red stone in your mouth as you speak, and no one will be able to refuse you.

And anyone who carries the white stone will never suffer from thirst ~ and this I know for certain to be true, for I was told it by a traveller who carried one with him on many difficult journeys.

The Eagle Stone~

This is a round stone, and is called the Eagle Stone because if an eagle finds one she will carry it to her nest.

It contains another stone within it, and either you may hear the second stone rattling loose within the first (which is the rarer kind), or if the stone is split open you may see the second stone growing in a hollow within it.

The virtues of the Eagle Stone are~

It will protect a woman who is with child from miscarriage.

If you wear it touching your left shoulder, you will have the love of your husband or wife, or of anyone else you desire.

To recover the affection of a lover whose feelings have cooled towards you ~

Carry a root of the herb Tormentil.

(And this root also has another virtue, which is, that if a piece of it is put upon an aching tooth it will ease the pain.)

Or take the blade
bone of a chicken, and
stick nine pins through
it, and lay it in a fire
upon the red hot
embers.

Then say :

May the one
That I desire
Burn with love for me
As this bone
Burns in the fire.

(Or you may use an apple or onion instead of the chicken bone.)

Or cast salt upon a fire on a Friday (which is the day ruled by the planet Venus) and say:

It is not this salt
I wish to burn,
But my lover's heart
I wish to turn.

A Potion to Induce Love ~

Take
   periwinkle
   houseleek
   earth~worms
and pound them up
well together.

   But some lovers are
better lost than won,
and magic can advise
you which kind yours
may be.

To discover if your lover will be faithful~

Put two hazel nuts in a fire.

If they burn up brightly and jump together, your lover will always be faithful to you.

But if they crack and jump apart your lover will prove to be a cold~hearted deceiver.

To have answers to questions of love, marriage and so forth~

When you have acquired some skill in the art of magic, there is a way to discover if a marriage will be happy, or, indeed, if any venture will be fortunate, and much else besides.

Take a hen's egg, and make a hole in the shell, and let a

quantity of the white
of the egg fall into a
bowl of water.

Place the bowl in
bright sunlight, and
you will see the white
of the egg become like
smoke or skeins of
white wool.

And by the shapes it
forms, you will see the
answers to whatever
questions anyone may
ask you.

Or you may use the
blade bone of a sheep,

and hold it before a
candle flame, and you
will see shapes within
the bone that will reveal
to you whatever you
wish to know.

(And since this may
be done by night, it
may be preferable if
your clients desire
secrecy ~ or are the
kind who jest at
magic by daylight,
but are more willing
to acknowledge its

power once the hours of darkness are upon them.)

And you must not think (as those who fear magic do) that by such divination you may foresee misfortunes that cannot be prevented. Magic would be a poor profession if that were so! No~ like a physician, if you discover that some affliction threatens your client, you must also find a remedy.

To give you an example~

Elizabeth Dunlop
and Agnes Blair ~

The wise woman
Elizabeth Dunlop had a
client named Agnes Blair,
who was betrothed to
the Laird of Baidland.
Elizabeth was told
by her familiar spirit
Tom Reid (who had
once been a mortal
man, but became a
Lord of Elfland after
he was killed in battle)

to warn Agnes that
if she married the
Laird she would die.

So Elizabeth had many
earnest discussions
with Agnes and
her family; and at
length it was decided
that instead of Agnes
her sister Margaret
should marry the
Laird. And that proved
to be a very happy
solution, much to the
satisfaction of all
three young persons.

The Circle ~

There is a form of magic much favoured by magicians, and which Honorius says is the very essence of the art, which is the Circle.

And I would not have you think that any magician has a skill that is denied to us craftsfolk; so I will tell you how you may use a Circle to discover a thief.

Draw the Circle on the ground in a wood under a fruit-bearing tree, such as a hawthorn or an elder tree. You should sweep the ground clear of leaves and twigs, and then inscribe the Circle in the earth using a new white-handled knife. And the Circle should be about one pace across.

Then make another
smaller circle within it,
and divide that circle
into four parts with
a cross. And the arms
of the cross should
point North, South,
East and West.

Then where each
line meets another
you must draw a small

cross, and between the inner and outer circles you must write these Sacred Names of God: ADONAY, EGYRYON, SOTHER, EMANUEL; drawing a cross between them.

Place a bowl of water in the centre of the Circle; and write the name of each person suspected of the theft on a small piece of paper and enclose it in a ball of clay.

Cast these balls of clay into the water; and the first that opens up will reveal the name of the thief.

To force a thief to confess and return what he has stolen ~

Take some of the white pigment that is made when silver is smelted, and mix it with the white of an egg, and use it to paint a picture of an eye on a piece of parchment.

Stick it on the wall, and take a nail made of brass and a hammer made of yew, and drive the nail into the eye and say:

I conjure whoever is guilty of this theft, by these Sacred Names of God, SABAOTH, KYRYOS, ANEPHENETON, that his pain will never cease till his eye is cast out or he confesses.

But if you help folk
to recover their stolen
goods, you may find
yourself in peril from
the thieves' anger.
When Elizabeth Dunlop
discovered the thieves
who had stolen a
plough, they seized
her and dragged her
before the Bishop of
Glasgow.

Elizabeth admitted
that the spirit Tom
Reid revealed the
names of the thieves

to her, and so (alas) she was indicted for witchcraft.

And I have no doubt that the thieves were handsomely rewarded for delivering her up, rather than punished for their crime.

But perhaps we should not be surprised at this, as a bishop in his palace or a magistrate in his hall knows that he is safe from

any common thief.
But a witch creeping
in through the key-
hole is another matter.

To protect cattle, horses
&c from thieves ~
   Say this charm:

Our Lord was born
In a cattle shed,
The beasts gave their hay
To be his bed;
Our Lady saw a thief
And said:
Stand, thief, stand~
You must stare

Like a stoat
And stand fixed
Like a tree
Till you have counted
Every grain of sand,
Every star in the sky,
Every drop in the sea.

To find something
that is lost, or money
or treasure hidden
buried in the ground~

Draw this pentacle
on parchment using
ink to which you have
added a few drops of
blood from a black
puppy:

Hang it round the neck of a white cockerel, and when you release him he will go to the place where the thing that is lost or hidden may be found, and he will stand there and crow.

If you suspect that a beast has been bewitched~

Shed some of his blood on to straw and burn it, and the shape of the witch will appear in the smoke.

Or there is another way (which is best if the one bewitched is human)~

Take a marigold flower, the leaf of a bay tree, a wolf's tooth; bind them all together

with yellow thread
and put them under
your pillow.

Then you will see the
witch in a dream.

(But if the wolf was
killed for his tooth it
will have no virtue.)

To turn the evil spell back on the witch~

Half fill a strong earthen bottle with the urine of the person or beast bewitched.

Add nine nails or pins and a handful of salt.

Stop it up with clay, and keep it warm over the fire.

And this will cause the witch great pain and difficulty passing water.

Magic Squares ~

There is a very curious way whereby you may draw upon the power of the Spirits of the Planets, which is to write a square of numbers.

And each Planet has its own particular square.

The Square of Saturn~

This is (I believe) the most ancient of these Squares.

6	1	8
7	5	3
2	9	4

And if someone seeks your help to overcome some difficulty or danger, it will prove excellent for the purpose.

You must inscribe it upon a thin sheet of lead (and if it is lead taken from a church, so much the better), on the day ruled by the Planet (which is Saturday).

Then burn the shed skin of a spider as incense, holding the Square in the smoke.

It should be worn in a little bag hung around the neck.

But if it is for a woman in childbirth it should be written on silk and tied to her right thigh.

The Square of Mars~

This is a powerful talisman for a soldier going into battle, and will make his enemies' weapons useless against him.

11	24	7	20	3
4	12	25	8	16
17	5	13	21	9
10	18	1	14	22
23	6	19	2	15

You must inscribe it upon a square piece of bronze.

And on the other side you must inscribe the Seal of Mars ~

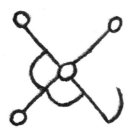

And the Seal of the Archangel of Mars (whose name is Samael) ~

And this must be done on the day ruled by Mars, which is Tuesday.

Then make a hole in one corner so that it may be worn upon a cord around the neck.

The Square of the Sun~

Many magicians say that this is the most powerful talisman of all.

6	32	3	34	35	1
7	11	27	28	8	30
19	14	16	15	23	24
18	20	22	21	17	13
25	29	10	9	26	12
36	5	33	4	2	31

You should write it upon a paper (which must be done on a Sunday).

And alongside it you must write the Seal of the Sun~

And the Seal of the Archangel of the Sun (who is Saint Michael)~

Then beneath it you must write these Sacred Names of God (and take care that you write them in three lines, exactly as I have done) ~

THEOS + TETRAGRAMMATON + YA

OCLEISTE + ELYOREM + MALOHT

ANETHI + NATHANOTHASY + IUESTRE

(And these names are from the 100 Sacred Names of God that Honorius was given by the Angel Hocroel.)

Then you must fold the paper up small and put it on a beam in the roof of the building you wish to protect.

And then the building and all who dwell in it ~ people and animals both ~ will be safe from all sickness and misfortune, and from fire, thieves, witchcraft and malevolent spirits.

Or to keep a fishing boat safe, you should

put the paper inside a
lobster's claw and fix
it to the mast.

Amulets Carved
from Gems ~

But of all those who
study the properties
of the stars and the
planets, the most
learned are found
amongst the people
known as Moslems in
the lands around the
Mediterranean Sea.

They are also unrivalled in their knowledge of the virtues of precious gems, and they use them to make talismans of such wondrous beauty that anyone would be happy to wear them as a jewel, even if they had no magical power.

Thus ~

A garnet carved with a picture of a lion when Mars is

ascendant (that is to say, when you may see it low in the sky in the east) will stop a wound from bleeding.

A piece of coral carved with a picture of a mouse between two cats when Venus is ascendant will drive away mice.

A piece of lapis lazuli carved with a picture of a serpent and a crescent moon when the Moon is ascendant will drive away snakes.

An emerald carved with a picture of a mouse when Mercury is ascendant will ensure that you will succeed in any trade.

A piece of rock crystal carved with a picture of a fox when Jupiter is ascendant will ensure that any enemies you may have will be afraid of you.

And it is said that these gems were valued for their magical powers by the Egyptians in ancient times.

The magician Honorius describes the appearance of the Angels of the Planets in his book.

♄

The Angels of Saturn are strangely long-limbed, like grass-hoppers, and look as if they are crafted out of beaten gold.

♂

The Angels of Mars flicker and gleam fiery red, like embers in the hearth.

♃

The Angels of Jupiter
look as if they are
carved out of blue
crystal.

♀

The Angels of Venus
are very elegant, and
look as if they are
made of snow.

☿

The Angels of Mercury
seem to be made of
white flame.

☾

The Angels of the Moon are like a dark storm cloud.

☉

The Angels of the Sun are very graceful, and clear and glittering like bright glass.

Magical Tools ~

You may have heard that magicians go about their work with the use of many tools, such as swords, flutes, rings, crystals and so forth ~ and that to set yourself up as a practitioner of magic costs more than to buy a horse.

But this is because magicians work with the aid of these Angels, and these exalted beings naturally expect to be entertained with a great deal of ceremony.

Daun Dhu, however, although he is a Lord of Elfland (and so I dare say somewhat above us mortals), does not need to be enticed with music, or impressed with swordsmanship. Indeed, he is ever quick to appear and offer me advice, even when I do not require it.

In general, we craftsfolk can make do with tools that are all around us for the taking.

If you wish to direct your magic, cut a hazel stick from the hedgerow for a wand.

And if you wish to bind your magic into some material thing, twist yourself a cord out of wool, and knot the magic into it.

The Friday Spell ~

But there is One whose power is greater than that of the stars and planets, and even the Archangels, and it is a strange contradiction that our Creator, who gives Life to all creatures, became one of the created, and suffered death. It is a great mystery to ponder upon.

But one thing is certain ~ he who willingly endured the sufferings of this world will not turn away from us when we entreat his help; which you may do by saying this charm ~

Our Lord sits
At his feast;
What has he
In his hand?
A fiery healing wand.
What has he
In his other hand?

Heaven's door key.
What is yonder
That shines so brightly?
Our Lady's son
Who is nailed
To the tree.
He is nailed sore
Through the heart
And the hand.
Gabriel lay down
To sleep
Upon the ground where
Our Lord did weep.
Our Lord
Came walking by.
Sleep'st thou,
Wakest thou, Gabriel?

No, Lord, I am struck
By stick and stake
So I can neither
Sleep nor wake.
Stand up, Gabriel,
And go with me ~
The stick nor the stake
Shall never hurt thee.

And this is called
the Friday Spell,
because on Good
Friday you should
say this charm over a
dead man's tooth, or a
piece of bread from
the Communion, and

put it in a little bag;
and whoever carries
or wears it will be
safe from all sickness,
misfortune or
witchcraft for
all the year
following.

For a cow, sheep &c~

   Say the charm over
a cross of rowan
wood and tie it into
her coat.

For a house, stable &c~

Say it over Saint
John's wort and salt,
enclose them in a ball
of clay, and hang it
up over the door.

To cure someone
already afflicted with
some illness ~

Cut a wand of
Virgin Hazel (that is,
of wood that has not
yet borne flower or
fruit), and say the
charm, and make the
sign of the cross with
the wand upon their
forehead.

And doubtless you
will soon find that
word of your skill

flies far and wide, and people will send to you for help from great distances; but even if they dwell a hundred miles away you may help them easily enough, for you may say the charm over a red woollen thread, tying nine knots in it as you do so, and then send this thread back to them by their messenger.

And if it is tied into the coat of the beast that is sick, or around the wrist of the person afflicted, it will cure them just as surely as if you had touched them with your wand.

And to ease the pain of childbirth~

Say the charm over a powder made from a dead man's bones, and put the powder under the woman's bed.

To heal an injured horse ~

  If a horse has wrenched a muscle or sinew;

  Take a knife and drive the point through a stem of briar to make a slit, leaving the briar still growing in the ground.

Say this charm:

The Lord of the Feast
Holds a length of briar
And says:
I conjure you
To close and seal.
As I conjure you
The horse will heal.

As the slit in the
briar closes up the
horse will be healed.

And take
care that the
horse is not ridden until
the slit is all sealed up.

To heal a burn~

   Say this charm:

Three Angels came from
Out of the East,
One brought fire
But two brought frost.
Out fire! In frost!

To stop bleeding~

   Say this:

Our Lord was born
In Bethlehem,
And was baptised
In the River Jordan;
The water stood;
So shall your blood.

To transfer an illness~

Sometimes it may be that the only way to heal someone is to transfer the illness to some other creature.

And to do this you must take a long cord of black wool, and make it into a loop and ask the sick person to step through the loop. If you then throw a duck or chicken or some other beast through the loop the sickness will be passed on to the beast.

It is also possible to pass an illness from one person to another — and with care this may be done so that the other person suffers no harm.

If a woman's children are all stillborn, she should take some earth from her child's grave, then weave a length of cloth, fold the earth into the cloth, and sell it. And if she sells it to a man, or to a woman who is past the age of childbearing, they will come to no harm by it.

A way to rid someone of a wart is to rub

the wart with a small
stone, put the stone in
a box and put the
box on a roadway.
And then the wart
will be transferred to
anyone who is so
foolhardy as to pick up
the box.

(And since such a
person is certain to be
ignorant of the ways
of magic, and to
think themselves
above the study of it,
you may be sure that

they will deserve
their misfortune.)

Jean Bodin, a very
learned man from
Paris, considered himself
a great expert on the
evils of magic (as he
saw them) and wrote
a book on the subject.
I believe that John
Starkie has read this
book many times, and
finds it more
entertaining than any
play. This Monsieur
Bodin claimed that

the only power healing magic has is to transfer an illness from one person to another.

And since this is the work of the Devil (he said) the illness is always transferred to a person of greater importance than the person who was cured ~ and so if a woman is cured, the illness is transferred to a man.

And then these gentlemen wonder why a woman might think the Devil has more sense than they do!

Whenever my friend the wizard Henry Baggilie heals any sick person, he is always struck down himself with whatever illness he has cured them of. But I fear there would be very few healers amongst us craftsfolk if that were always the case!

Another way to cure
a wart ~

Prick the wart with
a pin. Then rub the
wart with sheep's wool
found in a hedgerow.
Bend the pin and cast
it into a Holy Well.
Hang the wool in a
hawthorn tree.

To keep witches out of your house ~

Cut a slip of wood from an elm tree on Good Friday and carve three crosses into it and keep it by your hearth. Then no one who intends to use evil spells against you will be able to enter your house. And neither will any Familiar Spirit they send against you.

To repel a raid by
pirates~

   Soak a rag in
water, and strike it
upon a stone, and say:

I strike this rag
Upon this stone
To raise a storm
In our Lord's name.
   And there will be
such a storm that no
pirate ship will be
able to come near
shore.

To give sailors a fair wind for their ship~

On a day when the wind blows strong and steady, tie three knots in a rope.

And any sailor who has this rope from you may have a fair

wind for his ship by untying one of the knots.

(But be sure to warn him not to untie more than one knot.)

I have heard of a Cornish wizard, Peter Trevysard, who has such command of the winds and waves that he can stand on the shore and make a ship out at sea go wherever he wishes.

The Spell abracadabra~

Write out the word abracadabra 11 times on a piece of parchment.

Then take a sharp knife, and scratch out the last letter of the second line, then the last two letters of the third line, the last three letters of the fourth, and so on~

abracadabra
abracadabr
abracadab
abracada
abracad
abraca
abrac
abra
abr
ab
a

And you may use
this spell to rid yourself
of an illness or any
other unwanted thing.

The Crucifixus Spell~

There is a charm in Latin, which is~ Crucifixus hoc signum vitam eternam.

And by this charm you may obtain food or drink, or any other needful thing.

To have good fortune~

There is another Latin charm, which you should write on a piece of paper in the shape of a square~

```
S A T O R
A R E P O
T E N E T
O P E R A
R O T A S
```

And it will bring good fortune to anyone who carries it.

Or wear a ring made from a nail from a horse shoe.

Or wear a
mandrake root
in your hat.

(And this root bears
a most wonderful
resemblance to a human
figure. And if you boil
it in wine anyone who
drinks it will fall into
a deep stupor, and
will not wake though
his leg were cut off.)

The Magical Virtues of Beasts ~

(A subject both marvellous and profitable.)

The Mole ~

If you carry a mole's foot in your purse you will never want for money.

If you carry a mole's skin no one will be able to rob or cheat you.

To cure toothache or
any other pain in the
head or face~

Take

a mole's foot
Saint John's wort
(dried until it is red
like blood)
chervil
dill
fennel

Mix them all together
with hog's dung, wrap
them in linen, and
bind it around the head
of the afflicted person.

The Moorhen ~

A remedy for cramp, pain or stiffness in the hands is to carry a moorhen's foot.

(Or wear a ring made from a dead man's bone.)

The Bee~

Three bees, put in a little bag and hung up in a house, will bring prosperity to all who dwell there.

The Swallow~

When you sell cattle, if you tie a swallow's feather into the beast's coat you will be sure to get a good price.

The Sheep ~

There is a bone in the mouth of a sheep that is shaped like a hammer, and anyone who carries it will be safe from drowning.

The Mule ~

The mule is by her nature infertile. And so if you take shavings from a mule's hoof, burn them to ashes and swallow

them in a drink,
it will prevent
you from
conceiving
a child.

The Weasel~

If you carry the
tail of a weasel (but
be sure you do not
otherwise harm him,
but let him run free
again) dogs
will not
bark at
you.

The Adder ~

There is a ring of a blue colour, with the figure of a snake within it, and adders make it by breathing upon a hazel wand. And water poured over this ring will cure the bite of a snake, or of a mad dog, or festering wounds, or any other kind of poison.

The shed skin of an adder, fixed to a beam, will protect any building from fire.

But tying a knot in the shed skin of an adder is a way to cause impotence.

The Oyster ~

Another way to keep a building safe from fire is to make a talisman by writing

the Sacred Name of
God AGLA upon an
oyster's shell.

The Toad~

   If you hang a toad
up over an oyster's
shell, venom will fall
from him into the
shell, and this venom
is a medicine for
fevers and the falling
sickness.

The Cat ~

Of all creatures, the one that has the greatest virtue is the cat. For she is in herself a kind of talisman, drawn by the hand of God, that attracts good fortune to any place she dwells, and repels any evil.

(And such is her power to bring success to any magical operation that she is as effective an assistant as any spirit.)

Thus it is, that even when she is dead, if you fix her corpse above the doorway of a building, or in the roof, within the wall or under the threshold, it will ward off any rat, mouse or other thieving creature, or any malevolent spirit.

A charm for taking
the shape of a hare ~

I shall go into a hare
In sorrow and pain
And bitter care.

A charm for taking
the shape of a crow ~

I shall go into a crow
In sorrow and pain
And bitter throe.

A Flying Horse ~

Take a bundle of hay and say this charm:

Horse from hay,
Fly, horse, fly,
Away, away!

And the bundle of hay will be transformed into a horse.

You may ride this horse at great speed wherever you wish, and even fly through the air.

If you wish to find something that is lost or stolen, the horse will take you there.

Or if you wish to learn something that is happening some distance away, you may fly over the place without being observed.

And if you wish to discover something that happened in the past, the horse will take you not only to the place but also to the time it happened.

Some people say that it is your spirit that rides the horse, while your body sleeps. But so long as you achieve what is necessary, what does it matter?

Places to Acquire Magic ~

Another use for your enchanted horse is to fly to a place where you may acquire magic.

In a place called Benevento beyond Rome there is a walnut tree where many folk go to be given magical power.

And some say that the power comes from the tree itself, while others say it is given by a serpent who lives in the tree.

In some places (such as Cornwall, I have heard) there are heaps of great stones piled up by the giants in ancient times, with the topmost stone placed so that it rocks like a boat at sea.

And a way to gain magical power is to touch one of these rocking stones nine times at midnight.

Amulets from the Sea Folk ~

There is a place much like Elfland under the sea, and upon the shore you may sometimes find gifts from its people.

There is a kind of nut, shaped like a kidney (which some people call Elves' Kidneys, or Mary's Kidneys), and it is an amulet of great help to any woman in childbirth.

Or you may find a
strange little bag,
that seems to be
made of parchment or
very thin leather.
(Some say these are
the purses of the Sea
Folk.) And this will
bring you prosperity
and good fortune.

And it seems that
the Sea Folk sometimes
drill holes through
small stones, perhaps
to make weights for

their fishing nets. And one of these, carried on a fishing boat, will ensure a good catch and keep the boat safe from shipwreck.

These Sea Folk sometimes appear on land in the shape of seals. And if you help or please them in some way, they have it in their power to give you the gift of healing.

But they may also try to carry you away with them to their land beneath the sea.

I have heard of one wizard who was so entranced by the singing of one of these seal women that he had waded up to his shoulders in the sea before the barking of his dog woke him from the enchantment.

Daun Dhu has asked
me several times to go
with him to Elfland.
He says it is a wondrous
place, with feasts,
music and dancing. I am
sometimes tempted, but
the strangeness of it
daunts me.

Also, I fear I might
not be able to return,
and I would be sorry
to leave my brother
William and my friends,
and my old cat Tibb,

and the fine geese I
have this year.

I think Pendle Forest
is a fair enough place
for me ~ though it
would be better still if
some of its folk were
elsewhere.

The Frozen Mercury of the Alchemists~

You may have heard of people called Alchemists, who practise a kind of science that requires many strange vessels of metal and glass, and even stranger substances to be prepared in them. This involves these Alchemists in much expense, and all too often all their efforts and hopes are destroyed in an explosion.

However, one of these Alchemists, named Francesco Prelati, was also a magician of some skill, and by enlisting the help of a spirit he succeeded in making a black powder, which these Alchemists call Frozen Mercury.

It is said that this powder will cure any sickness and protect whoever carries it from any danger.

And I have met some wizards who claim to have some of this powder, made by Francesco Prelati himself (though he has been dead two hundred years).

Justice and Revenge ~
To cast down someone
who does not deserve
high office ~

Many people (alas)
contrive to get positions
of wealth and power
though they have neither
wit nor wisdom ~ indeed,
nothing but a high
opinion of themselves.

And by their folly
and injustice they cause
great misery to us
lesser folk (as they
think us).

But always remember that we are not as far below them as they think ~ certainly, not too far to take action against them.

Which you may do with the help of magic as follows ~

Take a sheet of brass, as thin as you can find.

Cut and fold it to make the shape of a man, hollow inside.

Fill the inside of the figure with bay leaves and wormwood, dried thoroughly.

Set fire to the herbs.

And he will find that the cares of his Office so eat into his entrails that he can no longer endure it.

To strike down an enemy ~

(And this is a skill that I must tell you of, though it grieves me that it is necessary.)

Make a figure of clay, as like in shape to the person you wish to hurt as you can fashion it.

And to make your enemy ill in whatever part of the body you wish, take a pin and stick it into that part of the figure.

Then wrap the figure in cloth taken from a grave and bury it in some foul, polluted place.

But when you wish to return the person to health, dig up the figure and take out the pin, and wash the figure in water from a spring.

But if you wish to take away your enemy's life, place the figure in a fire until it is all consumed away.

I had thought to make this the end of my little book about the Art of Magic, but when I showed it to Daun Dhu he said:

I wish, Jennet, you had not written that magic has the power to do harm. Surely that will seem to justify this outcry against witches that has the country all stirred up? It would have been better to say that magic should only

be used for healing,
and for protection
against misfortune, and
so forth.

So I replied: That is
easy for you to say,
when you live in
Elfland! In this sad
world where I and my
neighbours live, people
find that they have
enemies through no

fault of their own. And if those enemies harm them, or threaten to harm them, surely they should have the power to strike back?

And if I turn away someone who asks me to witch his enemy, and so he attacks him with a mattock instead, is that a better solution?

Then I shall teach you one last piece of magic (Daun Dhu said). And though it may seem so slight that it is hardly worth learning, you may find it more valuable than you expect.

If you carry a sprig of the herb betony, it will give you the courage to face any difficulty, however daunting it may be.